Songs for Keira
Poetry
To Grow With

By Sue Whittaker · Illustrated by Gina Harfman

For Keira

Order this book online at www.trafford.com/07-2159

or email orders@trafford.com

Most Trafford titles are also available at major online book retailers.

Note for Librarians: A cataloguing record for this book is available from Library
and Archives Canada at www.collectionscanada.ca/amicus/index-e.html

Printed in Victoria, BC, Canada.

ISBN: 978-1-4251-4992-5

*We at Trafford believe that it is the responsibility of us all, as both individuals
and corporations, to make choices that are environmentally and socially sound.
You, in turn, are supporting this responsible conduct each time you purchase a
Trafford book, or make use of our publishing services. To find out how you are
helping, please visit www.trafford.com/responsiblepublishing.html*

*Our mission is to efficiently provide the world's finest, most comprehensive
book publishing service, enabling every author to experience success.
To find out how to publish your book, your way, and have it available
worldwide, visit us online at www.trafford.com/10510*

www.trafford.com

North America & international
toll-free: 1 888 232 4444 (USA & Canada)
phone: 250 383 6864 ♦ fax: 250 383 6804
email: info@trafford.com

The United Kingdom & Europe
phone: +44 (0)1865 722 113 ♦ local rate: 0845 230 9601
facsimile: +44 (0)1865 722 868 ♦ email: info.uk@trafford.com

10 9 8 7 6 5

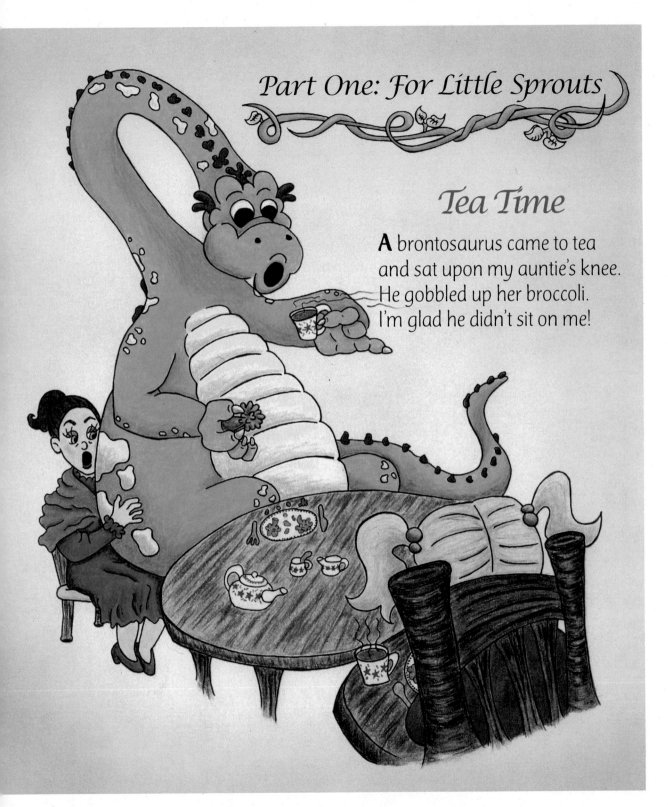

Part One: For Little Sprouts

Tea Time

A brontosaurus came to tea
and sat upon my auntie's knee.
He gobbled up her broccoli.
I'm glad he didn't sit on me!

Buddy

So there's just one kid,
living in this house.
I think I need a buddy.
A dog?
A cat?
A mouse?

How about a dragon?
NO!
Might set the house on fire.
But . . . the dinosaur who came
to tea,
was funny
and playful
loved games
and sang songs;
was helpful and caring,
he knew right from wrong.
He never got bored,
was high energy,
and if that's not enough,
he loved broccoli!

I think I'll call him Buddy.
He'll be great company.
A friend that I can count on
to spend his time with me.

Glorious Food

Potatoes and carrots, zucchini and peas.
No more veg-e-tubles please!
But then dessert is served and Wow!
Keira's really hungry now!

Sugar my Tea

Butter my bread
butter my bread,
butter my bread
and I'll get out of bed.

Sugar my tea
sugar my tea,
sugar my tea
and I'll sit on your knee.

Take off my shoes
take off my shoes,
take off my shoes
and I'll go for a snooze.

Give me a hug
give me a hug,
give me a hug
and I'm snug as a bug.

Shock Frock

Keira Bean went to town
wearing a beautiful emerald gown.
It knocked the boys right off their feet.
A sight like that is hard to beat.

The Training Blues

When I refuse to use the potty
Mommy frowns and says I'm naughty.
I JUST can't get the hang of it;
when to play and when to sit.

Bad Kitty

The cat is on the screen,
the cat is on the screen!
A glass of water
really ought-er
send her scampering.

A spider's on the door,
a spider's on the door!
Get a swatter
and that ought-er
finish him for sure.

June Bug

There's a June bug
upside down,
wiggling all its
legs around.

There's an earthworm
in a muddle,
came up underneath
a puddle.

Pill bug curling
in a ball.
Caterpillar,
watch him crawl.

Mommy's declared
war
on slugs.
Must be hard
to be a bug.

Round and Round

Plant a seed
in the spring
you can grow
most anything.

Summer is
the perfect time
to watch
the honeysuckle climb.

Leaves turn red
and pumpkins glow,
when autumn brings
a hint of snow.

In the winter
Nature rests
and robins plan
their summer nests.

Then the sun
comes back to kiss
Keira's cheeks,
that lucky miss!

I Love The Moon

I love the moon,
I love the moon.
The moon is so tenderly
lovely.

I love the sun,
I love the sun.
The sun is so radiantly
lovely.

I love my dad,
I love my dad.
My dad is so awesomely
lovely.

I love my mom,
I love my mom.
My mom is so comfortably
lovely.

Colour Commentary

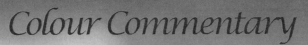

The only frog I've ever seen was one inch long and very green.

The cows I watch while traveling by, are black and white with big brown eyes.

The sky is blue, the moon is...cheesy. An orange is orange so that is easy.

The sun is yellow, tongues are pink. Blood is red — enough, I think!

Jump and Run

Run and jump,
jump and run,
through the rain
and in the sun.

Play and laugh,
laugh and play,
I will copy
what you say.

Sing and dance,
dance and sing,
whirl and spin,
twirl and swing.

Now I'm dizzy,
time to stop,
catch my breath
then hop, hop, hop.

Look at me,
I'm a frog
leaping on
an old brown log.

Think I'll turn
into a fish.
Watch my shiny
tail swish.

Back on land
I'm crawling up.
Now I'm a
German Shepherd pup.

Run and jump,
jump and run,
through the rain
and in the sun.

14

The Entire Routine

Supper tonight
was a messy affair.
She had squash in her ears
and gravy in her hair.

I'm thinking we'll need
the entire routine;
soap, shampoo and water
to get Keira clean.

Rub - a - dub

Turn on the water,
fill up the tub.
Climb in fast,
Rub – a – dub!

Tilt your head back
pour shampoo.
Here it comes;
boo hoo hoo!

Rinse the suds out,
squeaky clean.
Here's our shiny
Keira Bean.

Lucky Ducky

Sitting in the bath
playing with my ducky.
Teaching him to swim;
what a lucky ducky.

Splashing in the bath,
Oh, here comes the doggie.
Wow, he jumped right in with me!
What a soggy doggie!

Eeny Meeny

Eeny meeny miney mo,
kiss your finger,
kiss your toe.

Eeny meeny miney me,
bend your elbow,
bend your knee.

Eeny meeny miney may,
we could make up
rhymes all day.

Eeny meeny miney min,
is that a dimple
on your chin?

Countess Keira Bean

Count your fingers one to ten.
One, two, three, four, five,
Six, seven, eight, nine, ten.

Now count them backwards once again.
Ten, nine, eight, seven, six,
Five, four, three, two, one.

Now you've done that, I suppose,
you can count upon your toes.

Would you like to count my hair?
Mommy,
Please!
Let's not go there!

Snowflakes Falling

Snow flakes falling
on your tongue,
lick 'em up
yum, yum, yum!

Snowflakes falling
on the town,
dressing it up
in a clean white gown.

Snowflakes falling
on my dad
shoveling walks
and steps like mad.

Snowflakes falling
on the tree,
covering it
splendidly.

Snowflakes falling
everywhere.
Glad I've got
long underwear!

My Mommy Says

My mommy says
we'll have special treats
when Christmas comes,
when Christmas comes,
like turkey and stuffing
and homemade sweets,
when Christmas comes,
when Christmas comes.

My daddy says
we'll hunt for a tree,
when Christmas comes,
when Christmas comes,
up on the tree farm
with snow to our knees,
when Christmas comes,
when Christmas comes.

My Grandma says
she'll knit me mitts,
when Christmas comes,
when Christmas comes,

with stripes of red
and thumbs that fit,
when Christmas comes,
when Christmas comes.

We're all excited
and counting the days
'til Christmas comes,
'til Christmas comes.

Except for Grandpa
and he just says,
"HUMBUG!"

We've Got a Secret

Daddy told Mommy
and Mommy told me,
but it's still a secret
between just us three.

I didn't tell Billy
so he couldn't tell Lee
so no one else knows
but the green apple tree,
that up in its branches,
as high as can be,
there are four little
'somethings'
that no one can see.

They're tucked in a nest
and one day they'll fly free –
but no one will know
except my family.

Well – maybe the sun
and the moon, I'd agree,
and all of the leaves
on the green apple tree.

Grumpy Thoughts
From a Sleepy-time Gal

WHO invented bedtime?
I'd like to meet the guy.
I'd stuff him in a lonely room
and listen to him cry.

And what about the toothbrush?
WHOSE great idea was that?
Back and forth and up and down,
my teeth are wearing flat.

Oh no, here comes the facecloth,
invented by a witch.
In the ears and up the nose;
I'm developing a twitch.

And then, of course, the potty.
I sit until I'm numb.
Designed for pins and needles
and a ring around the bum.

23

Where is Keira Bean?

Keira Bean got lost one day,
no one here could find her.
Daddy looked in front of him,
Mommy looked behind her.

They searched the whole house,
up and down,
nowhere could they see,
the little girl they counted on
to serve them up their tea.

Daddy hunted in the east,
Mommy in the west.
Their house took on the aura
of a sad and empty nest.

"I'll check her bed," Daddy said,
"her blankie's there, that's strange.
It's never very far from her,
I'm sure that hasn't changed."

Oh! Keira Bean has just been seen
standing on her head,
balancing, perfectly,
underneath her bed.

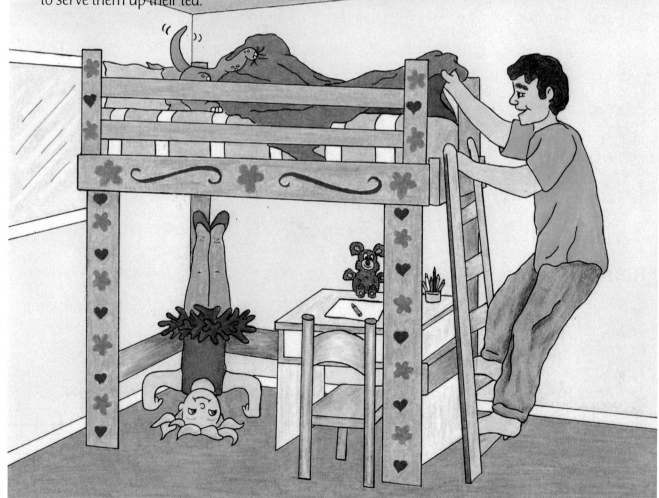

24

Send Keira Bean
to fetch the Queen,
we need her right away.
Make certain that
she wears a hat
and visits us in May.

Seat the Queen
by Keira Bean,
I'm sure she'll want to stay,
to celebrate her birthday
on the fourteenth day.

We'll keep the Queen
with Keira Bean
so they can chat and play,
and then we'll bake
the Queen a cake
on the twenty-fourth of May.

God Bless the Queen
and Keira Bean
and let them reign together,
in England
and in Canada,
forever and forever.

Daddy Has an 'Owie'

Daddy has an 'owie',
he really smacked his
thumb.
With a hammer!
It was awful!
Lucky he has Mom.

Mom got out the bandages,
good thing she's a nurse,
with ointment
and pain relief
she carries in her purse.

Daddy needs a nap now,
he's not a happy boy.
But in a while
he'll be able to smile,
'cause I lent him my favourite stuffed toy.

Keira Got a Stuffy Nose

Keira got a stuffy nose
and wasn't it a pain?
She had to use a tissue
again and again and again.

Then her throat got itchy.
She didn't like that much.
It hurt a lot to swallow
and even more to touch.

And then a strange thing happened,
around the seventh day.
She gave the cold to Daddy
and her troubles went away.

Now Daddy has a stuffy nose
and isn't it a pain?
Mommy says she'll take it
if he'll go to work again.

When I was one
my teething ring
was my favourite thing
that I would bring
to Granny's.

When I was two
I'd carry a drum,
Rum – tum – tum
whenever I'd come
to Granny's.

When I was three
I'd lug a bug
that I'd keep snug
in a coffee mug,
to Granny's.

When I was four
I loved a doll
a metre tall
that I would haul
to Granny's.

But now I'm five
and so I hike
or ride my bike
to Granny's.

Playschool Starts Tomorrow

Keira Bean looks worried,
we've never seen her glum,
but playschool starts tomorrow
and she'll have to leave her mom.

And won't her mom be lonely?
And won't her mom be sad?
She'll hate to leave her crying
and hanging on to Dad.

So now they've made a bargain.
Until her mom can cope,
she's allowed to tag along,
but just for the first week —
we hope!

First, Second, Third

From my very first birthday,
the picture I dread,
is the bowl of cake
upside-down on my head.

Then for my second, guess what?
Building blocks!
They sat in the corner while
I played with the box.

On my third birthday
a brand new red bike!
I raced up the street
with Sadie and Mike.

On my fourth birthday
I wanted to be
dressed up like
Snow White
or Sleeping
Beauty.

But on my fifth birthday
if I get my wish,
I'd like an aquarium
with tropical fish.

Just One More Sleep

Christmas is coming in twenty sleeps.
Daddy has strung the lights,
all around the eaves and trees
to brighten the long winter nights.

Christmas is coming in fourteen sleeps.
Mom's been baking like mad;
cookies and squares,
breads and cakes,
and butter tarts 'specially for Dad.

Christmas is coming in seven sleeps.
I sure love the Christmas tree.
Mom and Dad hung the garlands and lights
but they left the angel for me.

Christmas is coming in just one more sleep.
I'm listening so hard to hear a
sound of a hoof,
or a jolly HO HO
when Santa finds cookies from Keira.

Nightmares

A nightmare is a story
you tell yourself while you sleep.
A scary story that wakes you,
and you're all curled up in a heap.

Sadie had gorilla nightmares
and she screamed 'til her dad
came running.
They sat in a chair and cuddled
and thought of a plan that was
cunning.

Her daddy brought in a big stick
and stood it up, right in full sight there.
She could poke the gorilla a good one
if he showed up again in her nightmare.

Since then, Sadie's dreams have been happy.
The stories she tells in her sleep,
are playful, and sometimes quite funny.
The stick is a good thing to keep.

Sadie has a Tree House

Sadie has a tree house.
It used to be her brother's.
There's a sign that said,
'NO GURLS ALOUD'
but now we have another.

Our new sign says,
'YORE WELLCOME'
(especially with provisions)
like bubble gum,
potato chips,
and costume trunk additions.

You have to climb a ladder,
at first it can be scary.
I was nervous,
I confess,
but I didn't throw a hairy.

We have a
secret password,
you have to really yell it
to get inside
and join the fun
but you're not supposed to tell it.

The tree house has a window
and a broom to keep it neat,
a table and
some cushions,
and a rug to wipe your feet.

We practice songs and
act out plays,
and share our comics there.
It's absolutely
PERFECT;
a comfy, tree top lair.

Lightning and Thunder

A flash of lightning!
Next I hear
a crash of thunder
—outta here—

I'm racing down the hall
in fear.
Daddy calls out,
"Jump in here!"

He lifts the blankets
on his side,
I take a leap
and there I hide.

When my heart
slows down a notch,
Daddy says,
"Let's go and watch."

Through the dark house
hand in hand;
in the living room
we stand.

Flashing zig-zag
spears of light,
split the dark
and fracture night.

Thunder follows;
booming echoes
shaking floors
and rattling
windows!

"What makes
the boom?
Is someone mad?"
"Expansion of air,"
says my dad.

"Thunder never
hurt a thing,
but lightning carries
quite a zing."

"You're sure it's not
some monsters fighting?"
"No," says Dad,
"just thunder and
lightning."

34

On Tuesday I want to be Boss

On Tuesday I want to be boss!
I'll choose what I'm going to wear.
I'll have cookies for breakfast
and give my dad heck, first
when someone spills milk on my chair.

On Tuesday, the day that I'm boss,
no one but ME combs my hair!
I'll look just fantastic
without one elastic.
If it hangs in my eyes I don't care!

On Tuesday when I am the boss,
I might let my dad watch TV,
but I'll be the clicker
of the television flicker
and the shows will be chosen by me.

On Tuesday while I am still boss,
my folks have to go to bed first.
I'll stay up and make phone calls,
and popcorn and rum balls,
and eat 'til I'm ready to burst.

I know that I'll love being boss.
It will give my small ego a boost.
And they'll get to see
what it's like being me,
on Tuesday, when I rule the roost.

The Day After. . .

The day after I was the boss,
my parents said, "Never again!
We are glad to be rid
of that arrogant kid."
Now they call me Attila the Hen!

35

Sadie says she's grounded,
her brother's really mad.
She sneaked into his bedroom
and he told their mom and dad.

She knew that he'd been working
on a long hard Science project.
Sadie looked it over, thinking
she could make it perfect.

The project looked so boring
with diagrams and writing,
so Sadie thought she'd add some
colour - make it more exciting.

Jim mentioned it was 'fizz-ix'
so she started adding bubbles,
and bottles of pop and rainbows;
did they thank her for her troubles?

No a-pree-she-ay-shun!
Just a bunch of yelling!
Her brother Jim won't speak to her
but his dirty looks are telling.

Her mommy says, "Ignore him.
Jimmy needs his space."
But until Friday, Sadie's grounded.
She can't leave her place.

Good Old Days

When Daddy was a baby
did they have diapers then?
Did they feed him with a bottle
and keep him in a pen?

Were toys even invented
when Daddy was a kid?
Did they only play with marbles?
Is that what Daddy did?

Did he have to walk to school?
Five miles — in the snow —
in his brother's gumboots
at fifty degrees below?

Did they have porridge for breakfast
and then again for dinner?
Is that why they skipped lunch
and kids were so much thinner?

Why's it called the good old days?
We're lucky to be rid
of all that pain and suffering
when Daddy was a kid.

I Get the Picture

Measles,
chicken-pox
and mumps.
Itchy spots
and aching bumps.

Red, red skin,
a head that's hot . . .

Okay, okay!
I'll take the shot!

Now this is the life I want to lead,
lounging around in the bath.
I hope that it's possible, later on,
to include it, in my career path.

Keira – patra

They'll call me 'Keira – patra',
up to my neck in milk;
swanning around for the cameras
and famous for skin like silk.

I'll practice that pose with one foot up.
My toes will be pointed and cute.
I'll dab at my shin with a loofah
and really haul in the big loot.

Life in the bath; what a pleasure!
Stress-free and humming a tune.
But – WHOA! What's the chance that I'll end up
a premature, wrinkled old prune?!!!

Skills and Thrills

My very first time on the trampoline
and several times thereafter,
I needed umpteen spotters
to save me from disaster.

But once I got my balance,
I started having fun.
My interest in gymnastics
had definitely begun.

I landed on my knees and butt
and bounced back on my feet.
The day I did my first back flip
was pretty hard to beat.

Then we learned to jump in pairs,
in trios and quartets.
We mastered double bounces;
it's a day we won't forget.

Two went up while two came down.
That took coordination!
We laughed like loons while practicing
and developed lots of patience.

My friends have taught me many skills,
but none more satisfying
than performing on the trampoline,
the next best thing to flying.